GREAT BRITISH
inventions

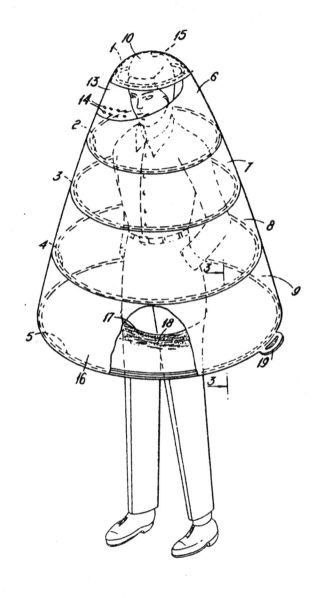

GREAT BRITISH
inventions

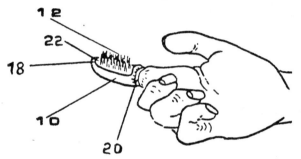

Selected and edited by Mark Tanner

FOURTH ESTATE • *London*

First published in Great Britain in 1997 by
Fourth Estate Limited
6 Salem Road
London W2 4BU

10 9 8 7 6 5 4 3 2 1

A catalogue record for this book is available from the
British Library.

ISBN 1-85702-734-5

Designed and typeset by Blackjacks, London.
Printed in Great Britain by The Bath Press, Bath

To Adam Gac,
the pilot who weathered the storm

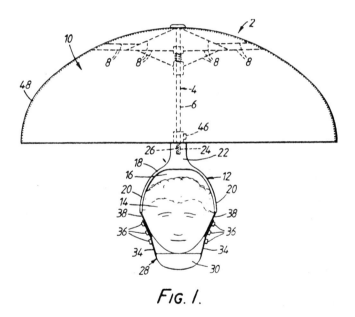

FIG. 1.

Contents

Introduction

The idea of the patent was developed many years ago in order to prevent Great British Inventors having their ideas stolen by someone altogether less honourable and decent than themselves.

Prior to the introduction of patents, one may have laboured long and hard developing an idea such as 'Inflatable Chamber-pots', 'Wearable Seating Apparatus', or any of the other marvellous inventions that appear in this book, only to find that some scoundrel had stolen the idea, produced it to world acclaim, and became immensely rich from the proceeds. It was to protect our geniuses from such appalling injustices that the system of patents was created.

The system has evolved considerably since its beginnings. Nowadays, one may register a patent for the princely sum of £25. In the first application the inventor needs to provide a drawing of their idea, along with an explanation of the thinking behind it. Why, for example, it is important to have a toothbrush, the handle of which can be chewed. If within twelve months the inventor is still convinced of the potential of his creation, he may proceed to the second stage. He then pays £130 to the Patent Office and the application is published and compared to similar inventions. The 'Nightmare Prevention Mattress', for example, will be compared to other mattresses that have been designed with that purpose in mind.

To complete the process, the inventor pays a further £130 and can make amendments to the original idea. In a typical case he may decide to improve the pump action of his faecal-collecting walking-stick, in order to distinguish it from other faecal-collecting walking-sticks. If the Patent Office is satisfied with the originality of the final application, a full patent will be granted. The inventor will thus be able to benefit from the fruit of his invention, preventing less savoury people taking advantage of the idea, and sending a message to the world that when it comes to ingenuity, Britain still rules the waves.

This book is a collection of such ingenuity. While other nations focus their energies on complicated new technologies, Great British Inventors, often working alone and with few resources, devise stunningly simple and original solutions to many universal, and some particularly British, problems. The cereal bowl designed to prevent your Cornflakes becoming soggy. A tip-up lavatory seat for the British tourist to take on foreign holidays. An umbrella in the form of a hat to free both hands on a rainy day. An alarm system to prevent people rocking on their chairs. A tie which can also be used to clean dirty spectacles.

All the inventions presented have at least reached the second stage of the application procedure. Some may already have been granted full patents and be in production; others, it is sad to say, may not have been so fortunate.

A POSTBOX

UK Patent Application

GB 2 284 015 A

Application published

24.05.1995

Application No

9420864.2

Date of filing

12.10.1994

Domestic classification

EX2 X10 X8
A5A A22

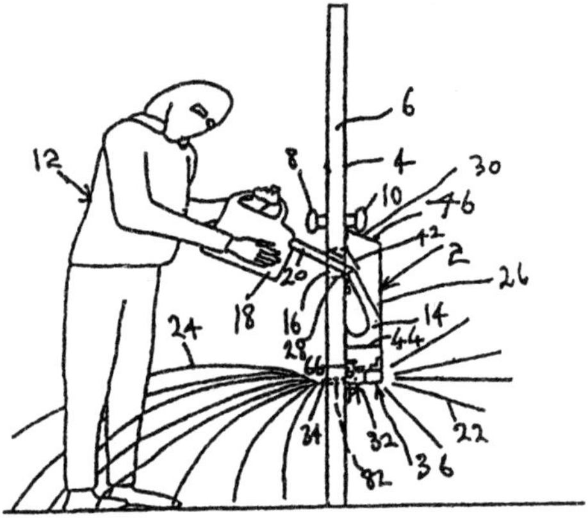

FIG 1

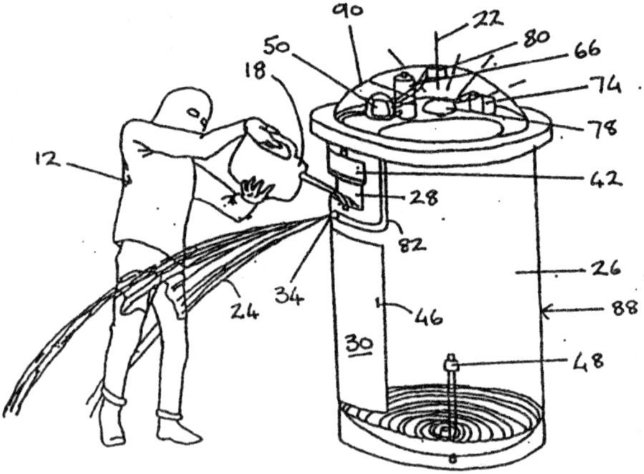

FIG 10

A Postbox

This invention relates to a postbox, for example a letterbox or a postal authority pillarbox.

Attacks on postboxes are a common occurrence. For example, vandals often put rubbish or unpleasant substances through letterboxes with a view to upsetting occupants of houses and offices. Sometimes the attack on the letterbox is malicious and sometimes the attack on the letterbox is more in the nature of a prank. In any event, damage is often incurred, together with owners of premises being upset and put to the inconvenience of having to clear up mess. It is an aim of the present invention to reduce this problem.

Accordingly, in one non-limiting embodiment of the present invention, there is provided a postbox comprising a body, a slot in the body for enabling postal items to be inserted into the body, a door for enabling postal items which have been inserted into the body to be retrieved, at least one defence mechanism for protecting the postbox consequent upon the postbox being subject to an attack, and at least one sensor means for sensing the attack and for causing the defence mechanism to operate.

Once the sensor means has been activated the alarm (22) is sounded and the closure flap (42) is released to seal the box, preventing further access by the attacker and starving any fire of oxygen. The dye discharge system is activated to mark the attacker to help in detection.

A Chair
for Coition

The present invention relates to a novel form of chair.

In the past chairs have been constructed with a seat, with one or more legs for supporting the seat at an elevated height, a back rest and possibly two arms. This chair is ideally suited for one person, but is not so ideally suited for two people.

If a man and a woman wish to have intimate relations on a known chair, they face the problem that the woman once astride the man will be unsupported, since there is no section for supporting her back. This makes the act of coition difficult and uncomfortable.

The present invention provides a chair comprising: a seat, support means for supporting the seat in an elevated position, a first back rest, and a second back rest.

In the preferred embodiment the seat is movable and means is provided to vibrate the seat. Preferably the means to vibrate the seat includes a motor controllable by a user of the chair. Preferably the motor is connected to a cam which engages a portion of the the seat, and the cam vibrates the seat on rotation. Preferably the chair comprises additionally a table mounted on an arm which is connected to one of the back rests.

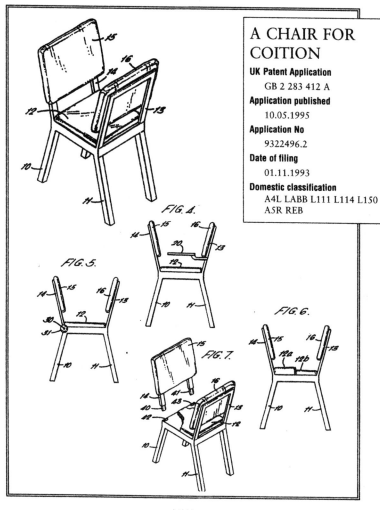

A CHAIR FOR COITION

UK Patent Application
   GB 2 283 412 A

Application published
   10.05.1995

Application No
   9322496.2

Date of filing
   01.11.1993

Domestic classification
   A4L LABB L111 L114 L150
   A5R REB

FIG. 4.

FIG. 5.

FIG. 6.

FIG. 7.

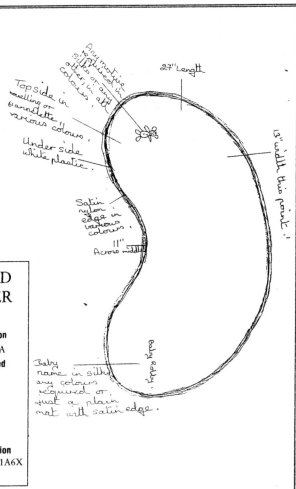

Any motive stitched in any other in all colours.

Topside in towelling or vianelette various colours.

27" Length

Under side white plastic.

13" width this point !

Satin nylon edge in various colours.

11"
Across middle

Baby Roby

Baby name in silk any colours required or just a plain mat with satin edge.

A LAP AND SHOULDER MAP

UK Patent Application
GB 2 284 142 A

Application published
31.05.1995

Application No
9324362.4

Date of filing
26.11.1993

Domestic classification
A3V V1A3A V1A6X
V7AX V7A2

A Lap and Shoulder Map

This is a kidney-shaped mat made up of towelling or flannelette with a plastic backing to protect clothing, with satin edge, and a motif, monogram or any design required for personal taste can be put on the mat face.

The idea is to put the mat onto Nanny, Grandad, Aunty, Uncle or any relative or friend of whom wishes to hold baby or burp baby.

The idea is to protect clothing in case of any mishap when relative or friend is holding baby.

There is already a prototype.

A Drink Container

This invention relates to a container for drink, more especially one for use by young children.

The present inventor has made a study of the circumstances surrounding such use of a drink container by a young child and has realised that the intensity of the child's interest depends upon various psychological factors, one being the interest of the object, and another, unobvious one, being the attractiveness of the object, the amount of love it generates in the child, its familiarity, the degree to which it actuates natural feelings of the child and/or perhaps other aspects.

Accordingly, the present invention provides a container for drink as claimed in Claim 1. It appears that a mouth is a familiar and welcome object to a young child, who will therefore retain such a drink container longer and more firmly than any other kind to be grasped by the child in its hands. The mouth may have pouting lips which lend themselves to ready sucking by a child. For older children a straw or similar drinking tube is more appropriate.

For young children, a particularly efficacious drinking tube is one that projects only slightly from the lips so that the child is substantially in a mouth-to-mouth kissing relationship with the lips when drinking.

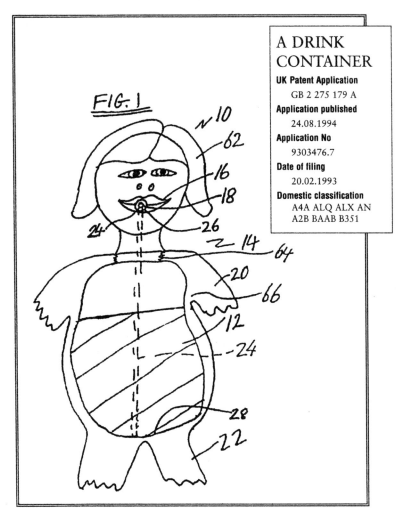

FIG. 1

A DRINK CONTAINER

UK Patent Application
GB 2 275 179 A

Application published
24.08.1994

Application No
9303476.7

Date of filing
20.02.1993

Domestic classification
A4A ALQ ALX AN
A2B BAAB B351

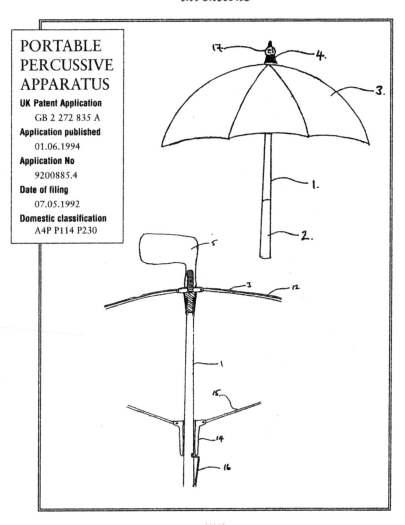

PORTABLE PERCUSSIVE APPARATUS

UK Patent Application

GB 2 272 835 A

Application published

01.06.1994

Application No

9200885.4

Date of filing

07.05.1992

Domestic classification

A4P P114 P230

Portable Percussive Apparatus

The invention relates to an article which is portable and capable of performing the function of an umbrella, comprising a shaft and, at either or both ends of the shaft, a fastening means which enables a canopy or alternative implement as required to be attached to or detached from the shaft to enable the apparatus to perform an alternative function. For example, a golf-club head.

The invention is designed to enable those who travel to have with them wherever they go, either on foot, in car, in a plane or by any other mode of transport, an instrument which is able to play a second role which will permit the traveller to partake of his work or recreational activity with the minimum of additional luggage or equipment as might otherwise be the case.

The invention thus has the advantage not only of being portable but also convertible to the instrument of one's work or hobby, whilst at the same time, prior to conversion, appears like and performs the function of an everyday item of need. To the City businessman, for example, this camouflage provides much-needed discretion without which a loss in credibility could result.

Spider Ladder

The invention relates to a Spider Ladder and more particularly to a Spider Ladder for attachment to a bath or basin.

The common house spider is commonly trapped within a bath or basin. This is mainly due to a spider's inability to negotiate or scale the smooth inner contours of a conventional bath or basin.

According to the present drawing, a thin flexible rubber strip (1) is attached to a suction pad (5). The suction pad is positioned on or near the top edge of a bath or basin and the Spider Ladder is allowed under gravity to follow the inner contours of a bath or basin until the free end is positioned at the inner base.

In order to prevent spiders from seeking refuge under the Spider Ladder the strip is made from a flexible material, preferably rubber or plastic. The width of the base assists a spider seeking refuge to find the Ladder quickly and climb the ladder faster.

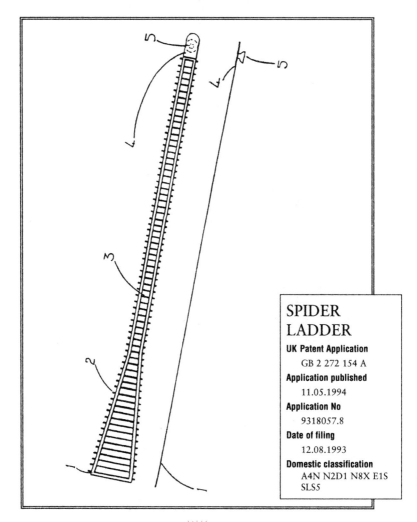

SPIDER LADDER

UK Patent Application
GB 2 272 154 A

Application published
11.05.1994

Application No
9318057.8

Date of filing
12.08.1993

Domestic classification
A4N N2D1 N8X E1S
SLS5

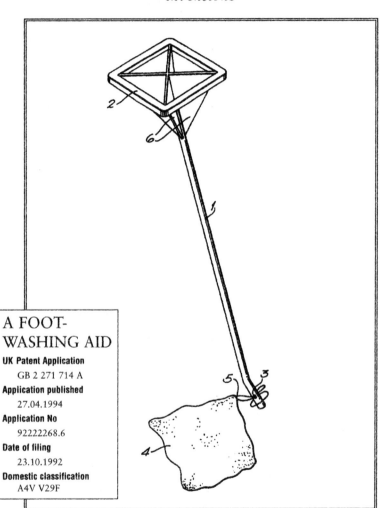

A FOOT-WASHING AID

UK Patent Application
GB 2 271 714 A

Application published
27.04.1994

Application No
92222268.6

Date of filing
23.10.1992

Domestic classification
A4V V29F

A Foot-washing Aid

It is an object of the present invention to provide an aid for use by an individual in washing and drying between the toes without undue bending by that individual.

According to the invention there is provided a toilet aid comprising a rod for use in association with a washing or drying cloth, said rod having a handle at one end and means at the other end to secure the said cloth.

In use, the rod acts as an extension to an individual's arm and permits the cloth to be drawn between the toes without undue bending from a seated position. The handle (2) is shaped and sized to permit two-handed operation, thus facilitating the provision of a slight twisting motion to the rod and the cloth if such is desired during the washing or drying stages.

The rod may be straight, but preferably the eyelet end is offest about 15° from the axis of the rod. This feature is particularly useful when toes tend to lie closely together or over each other in the manner known in some foot conditions. The action of drawing the offset end of the rod between the toes pushes the toes apart and facilitates the passage of the washing or drying cloth.

The overall length of the rod and handle can be varied but a convenient length would appear to be about 90cms.

Apparatus for Playing a Game

This invention relates to apparatus for playing a game.

Games such as billiards, snooker, pool and table tennis are played on purpose-built tables. When players tire of playing a game, the tables usually remain unused because they cannot serve any other function. The purpose-built tables are expensive items and they take up large areas. It is thus not desirable that the purpose-built tables should remain idle for long periods when they are not in use.

It is an aim of the present invention to reduce the above-mentioned problem. Accordingly, the present invention provides apparatus for playing a game, which apparatus comprises a playing-surface member which bears a predetermined game design for playing a predetermined game, the playing surface being removable and supported on support means whereby different playing surfaces for playing different games are playable on the same support means.

Thus lots of different games can be played on the same single support means so that the support means is able to be used more often than it would be if it were only for playing one game.

The playing board may include playing holes.

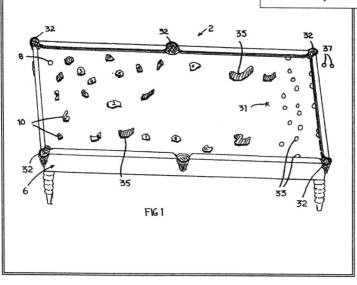

APPARATUS FOR PLAYING A GAME

UK Patent Application
GB 2 269 534

Application published
16.02.1994

Application No
9315462.3

Date of filing
27.07.1993

Domestic classification
A4L LAAQ L119 L145

FIG 1

A SLEEPING-BAG

UK Patent Application

GB 2 267 820 A

Application published

22.12.1993

Application No

9212813.1

Date of filing

17.06.1992

Domestic classification

A4G G10

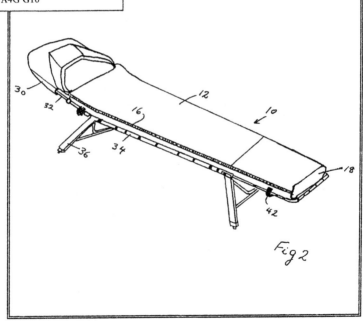

Fig 2

A Sleeping-bag

The present invention relates to a sleeping-bag.

In certain types of angling, it is necessary spend long periods waiting for a fish to bite. While waiting for a bite, in order to make himself as comfortable as possible the angler will often have a folding camp bed to lie on, a tent to keep him dry and shelter him from wind and a sleeping-bag to keep him warm.

Sleeping-bags are usually made from a nylon material. Though they are well suited for use on the floor, they are uncomfortable when used on a folding bed because they tend to slide on the bed and ruck up under the person lying in them. The problem for anglers is even worse because on certain occasions it may not be possible for the bed to be perfectly horizontal and the sleeping bag tends to slide downhill and eventually falls off the bed.

With a view to mitigating the foregoing disadvantage, the present invention provides a sleeping-bag having means for securing the sleeping-bag to the frame of a folding bed to prevent the bag from sliding relative to the bed.

A further problem which anglers face is that they need to be able to get out of the sleeping-bag and off the camp bed as quickly as possible when they hear an alarm from a bite indicator. It is not unknown for an angler in his haste, to get his feet caught in the sleeping-bag and drag it off the camp bed as he tries to place his feet on the floor.

Wearable Seating Apparatus

This invention concerns improvements in or relating to seating apparatus.

In many activities such as walking and hiking, fishing, or boating, a person wishes to sit down at some point. However, it may not be convenient or possible for that person to have a chair with them. Accordingly, the person will problably have to sit on the ground which is often wet and/or dirty and also not particularly comfortable.

According to the present invention there is provided seating apparatus which can be worn by a person, the apparatus comprising a support member and means permitting the support member to either be carried in a stowed position or to be positioned such that the person can sit thereupon.

The support member is preferably padded. The apparatus preferably comprises a belt which can be worn around a person's waist. An intermediate member preferably extends from the belt, downwards in use, and on the free end of which is provided the support member. The support member and intermediate member are preferably pivotally connected.

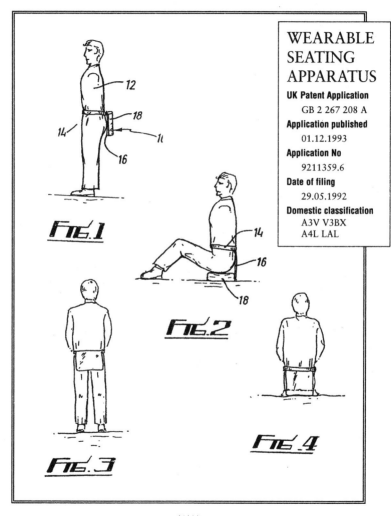

WEARABLE
SEATING
APPARATUS

UK Patent Application
GB 2 267 208 A

Application published
01.12.1993

Application No
9211359.6

Date of filing
29.05.1992

Domestic classification
A3V V3BX
A4L LAL

Fig.1

Fig.2

Fig.3

Fig.4

SHOWER AND DRYER UNIT

UK Patent Application

GB 2 266 662 A

Application published

10.11.1993

Application No

9209649.4

Date of filing

05.05.1992

Domestic classification

A4V V29F

A4N N2B

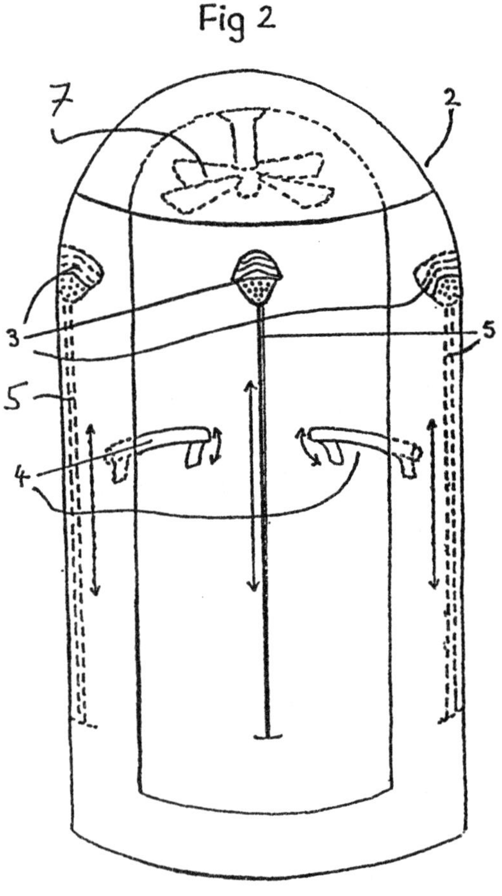

Fig 2

Shower and Dryer Unit

The everyday process of personal washing and drying is normally carried out using a bath or shower followed by rubbing with a towel over the body.

Drying by towel has the disadvantage of being less hygienic since the towel can transmit germs. This is obviously a significant consideration to organisations such as hospitals, old people's homes, health clubs and hotels, for example. Also, the time and expense involved in collecting, washing and replacing towels involves considerable expense and waste of energy.

There is also a safety problem with drying by towel. Bath and shower areas are surrounded by hard surfaces, and the floors are often slippery if damp. The physical movement necessary when drying by towel means there is an increased danger of a slip or a knock which could cause injury.

According to the present invention, there is therefore provided a dryer for a human or animal body, comprising a plurality of gas-directing means, for directing a drying gas at various parts of the body, overcoming the aforementioned problems.

Head Support for a Coffin

This invention relates to a head support for use in resting a head of a body of a deceased person in a coffin or casket (hereinafter referred to simply as a 'coffin') such that the head is position-supported particularly during transportation of the body in the coffin.

A problem arises in some areas/countries where, due to local custom, it is necessary to transport a body from a funeral undertakers where it has been embalmed, back to his/her former or relative's residence for the deceased to be viewed in the coffin with the lid removed. In the residence, it may be necessary for the coffin to be manhandled to an upstairs room. The steepness and narrowness of the stairs determines at what angle the coffin has to be positioned to pass thereup. During transportation and manhandling of the coffin, the head of the dead person can become displaced.

Heretofore, the head has been steadied by having support pillows; however, the availability and costs of the stuffing/packing for such pillows has lessened and become more expensive respectively. This is a disadvantage and the purpose of the present invention is to provide an alternative head support.

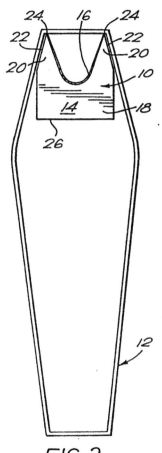

FIG. 2.

HEAD SUPPORT FOR A COFFIN

UK Patent Application

GB 2 266 293 A

Application published

27.10.1993

Application No

9208443.3

Date of filing

16.04.1992

Domestic classification

B8P PE2G PQ 100
A4L LABF L147
U1S S1276 S1462

A MIRROR

UK Patent Application
 GB 2 266 236 A
Application published
 27.10.1993
Application No
 9208913.5
Date of filing
 24.04.1992
Domestic classification
 A4V V26

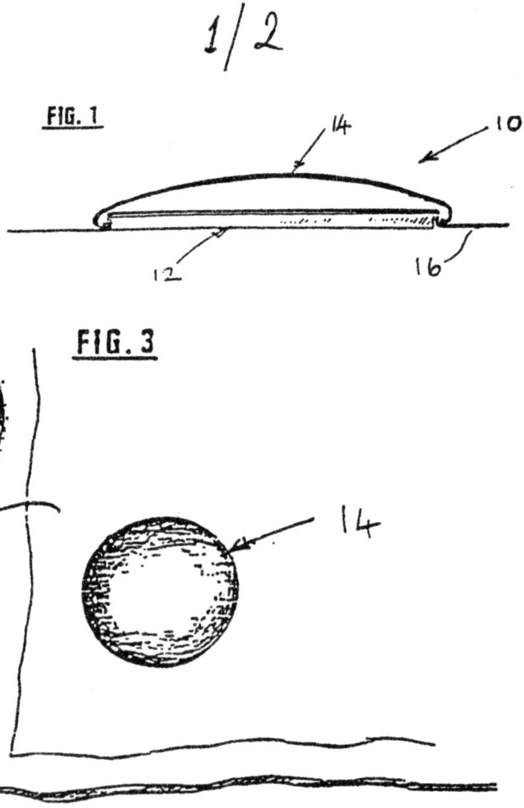

1 / 2

FIG. 1

FIG. 3

A Mirror

The present invention relates to personal mirrors.

It is common for people who are concerned about their physical appearance to carry about with them a mirror to check whether their make-up is correct or that their face is clean, for example. Separate mirrors can be dangerous to carry about in a pocket of clothing, perhaps in the case of a man for example, where a handbag is not normally carried. The use of a separate mirror can also be undesirably obvious and the user may want a means to check their appearance which is more discreet.

It is an object of the present invention to provide means for a person to check their appearance, and if necessary to clean their face, for example, discreetly.

According to the present invention there is provided a cloth such as a handkerchief to which is affixed a mirror. The mirror may be provided with means to enable it to be attached to the cloth in an easily removable manner so as to allow the cloth to be washed, the mirror itself to be cleaned and to permit the mirror to be transferable to other cloths.

The size of a mirror may be anything that is convenient, easily handled and easily concealed for example; a size within the range from 25 to 50mm may, for example, be found adequate. It must be stressed, however, that there are no restrictions on the size other than those relating to the use to which the combinations to be put and the requirements of the user.

A Cereal Bowl

This invention relates to a cereal bowl and, more especially, this invention relates to a cereal bowl for use in eating a cereal.

There are many types of cereals such as for example Cornflakes, Rice Crispies, muesli, porridge and a variety of proprietary cereals. The cereals are customarily eaten with milk. Those cereals which are of a crispy nature tend to become soggy if they are left in contact with the milk for more than a few seconds. This means that the cereal is not of a consistent quality from the start to the finish of eating. Many persons prefer crispy cereals rather than soggy cereals and thus the cereals which become soggy after the start of eating are often not acceptable to persons preferring crispy cereals.

It is an aim of the present invention to obviate or reduce the above-mentioned problem by providing a cereal bowl which enables crispy cereals to remain crisp from the start to the finish of eating.

The cereal bowl of the present invention is thus such that the cereal can remain isolated in the first part and the milk can remain isolated in the second part. During eating, the cereal can be scooped on to a spoon which can then be dipped into the milk in the second part of the cereal bowl. Alternatively, some of the cereal can be scooped into the milk and the milk and the cereal can then be scooped out with the spoon.

1 / 1

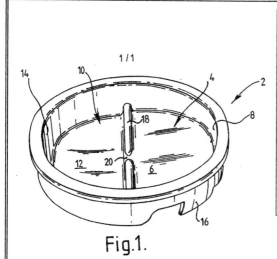

A CEREAL BOWL

UK Patent Application
GB 2 265 816 A

Application published
13.10.1993

Application No
9205663.9

Date of filing
16.03.1992

Domestic classification
A4A AG
UIS S1096

Fig.1.

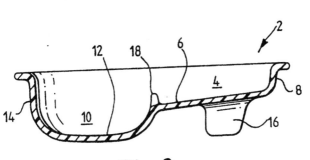

Fig.2.

SHOPPING AIDE

UK Patent Application
GB 2 263 862 A

Application published
11.08.1993

Application No
9121982.4

Date of filing
16.10.1991

Domestic classification
A4G G3
G4A ADT

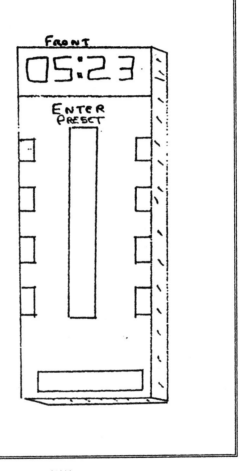

Shopping Aide

A self-contained unit designed to aid the shopper to buy selectively by budgeting accurately to their pocket. Therefore giving back the confidence to shoppers to buy in large stores again, of which they may have been scared by checkout horror bills.

This is a unit capable of being simply but accurately used. Firstly you enter the amount which you you wish to spend into the 'preset spending limit programme'. You then start entering the items' purchase price via the push buttons until, at such time you reach the preset spending limit, the unit automatically alerts you that this has been reached, so you can decide whether to carry on.

This unit may be temporarily or permanently attached to a shopping trolley or may be an integral part. For more freedom it may be attached to the customer by Velcro.

A Nightmare Prevention Mattress

(FIG. 1) It is comprised of a baby's cot mattress which is believed to offer more comfort to a small child that could be prone to shock suffered by the trauma of undergoing a nightmare situation, probably due over a certain period of time to the hardness of other cot mattresses.

(FIG. 2) A baby's cot mattress as claimed in Claim 1, with an appropriate recess (Fig. 2) to protect the main organ of the body (the heart), from excessive pressure.

(FIG. 3) A baby's cot mattress, as claimed in Claim 1 and Claim 2, which has in its construction, sloping sides which would gently restore the baby's body back to its position over the 'Recess', should it stray, in sleep.

(FIG. 4) A baby's cot mattress as claimed in Claim 1 and Claim 2 or Claim 3, which has incorporated into it, a baby 'Foot-Stop' device, which, when placed in a suitable position, should stop the said baby from sliding too far down the foot of the mattress. The 'Foot-Stop' is movable and is 'made' to interact with other parts of the mattress as the baby grows and in time reverts back to its initial position at the foot of the cot.

A NIGHTMARE PREVENTION MATTRESS

UK Patent Application

GB 2 263 399 A

Application published

28.07.1993

Application No

9225020.8

Date of filing

30.11.1992

Domestic classification

A4M MICX

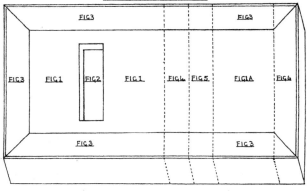

PANEL A
A NIGHTMARE PREVENTION BED
THE INITIAL POSITION

A PRAYER MAT

UK Patent Application

GB 2 263 003 A

Application published

07.07.1993

Application No

9222222.3

Date of filing

22.10.1992

Domestic classification

G4D DAC
  A4S SIC
   UIS S1204
S1220

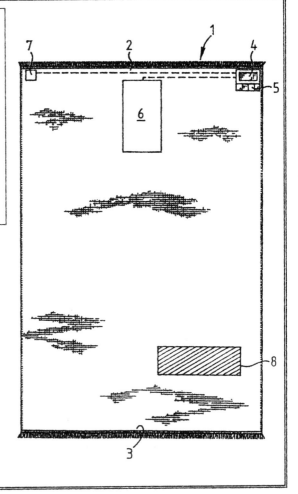

A Prayer Mat

This invention relates to a prayer mat.

During Islamic prayers worshippers carry out the following ritual:

Iqamah: Upright standing position facing the Kaba (Mecca) with feet apart.

Ruku: Bowing position with a straight back and hands on knees.

Sajda: Prostration on a prayer mat whereby the toes of both feet, knees, palms of both hands, the tip of the nose and the forehead touch the mat.

The sequence commencing with *Iqamah* and proceeding to *Ruku*, then to *Sajda* and finally back to the standing *Iqamah* position is called a *Rakat*. However, a *Rakat* is only completed if, during *Sajda*, the worshipper twice touches the mat with the forehead.

According to the present invention, there is provided a prayer mat comprising an electrical circuit, including means for supplying power to the circuit, a display for displaying in turn digits in a series of digits, a switch, and a counter for counting a sequence of operations of the switch and for controlling the display to display digits indicative of the sequence, so that the display indicates the number of *Rakats* carried out during prayer.

A Faecal-collecting Walking-stick

This invention relates to a device for the convenient removal and disposal of excrement faeces from public thoroughfares, parks and private gardens.

The problem of dog excrement is particularly obnoxious, both enviromentally and as a health hazard. Existing devices for removing the excrement are both messy and cumbersome, requiring shovelling into containers.

According to the present invention, the faeces are scooped up automatically, by means of a combined grabbing and suction action, into a self-sealing plastic bag, which is drawn out of sight into an unobtrusive receptacle. The whole device is in the form of a walking-stick which, even when filled with the collected excrement, can be used in a conventional manner to transport the excrement to a suitable depository, where it can be ejected from the walking-stick by a pump action of the handle.

The operation of the invention is such that no excrement is deposited on the device itself and it is performed entirely at arm's length. Further collections can be made by the simple process of reloading the walking-stick with a fresh plastic bag.

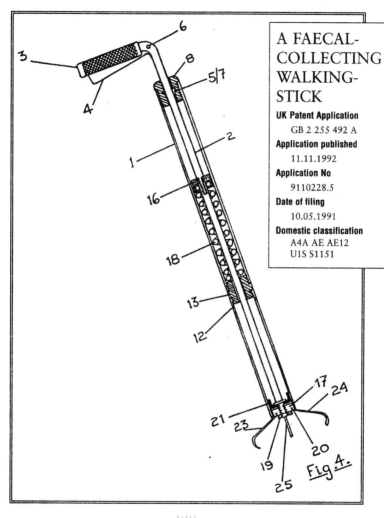

A FAECAL-COLLECTING WALKING-STICK

UK Patent Application
GB 2 255 492 A

Application published
11.11.1992

Application No
9110228.5

Date of filing
10.05.1991

Domestic classification
A4A AE AE12
U1S S1151

Fig.4.

INFLATABLE CHAMBER-POTS

UK Patent Application
  GB 2 255 011 A

Application published
  28.10.1992

Application No
  9208975.4

Date of filing
  24.04.1992

Domestic classification
  A4N N22

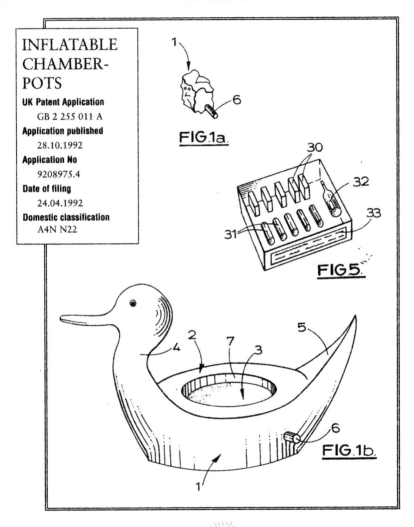

FIG.1a.

FIG.5.

FIG.1b.

Inflatable Chamber-pots

This invention relates to disposable chamber-pots.

Mothers will know very well that small children often want to go to the toilet at the most awkward times: in a crowded space; in the car; in the street. Small children have little foresight and just as little control, a parent often receiving only moments' notice of an impending need.

According to a first aspect, the invention comprises a disposable chamber-pot, or potty, which is inflatable from a deflated condition to an inflated condition of use. A parent puts the new, un-inflated pot, in their trouser or coat pocket when they go out with their small child. When the child needs the pot, and no conventional toilet is near enough, the parent takes out the pot, activates the cartridge 6, and within seconds the child has a pot.

Making the pot in the shape of a bird, dinosaur, or other animal with a head and tail may also reassure the the child.

According to a second aspect, the invention comprises a kit comprising a chamber-pot in accordance with the first aspect of the invention and absorbent material adapted to be put into the pot after use.

The pots of the figures can withstand the weight of a small child sitting on them, say 35kg. Pots for adults (for use when camping or in emergencies) are also envisaged.

Binge Beater Bracelet

The present invention relates to a device to aid persons trying to reduce their food intake, and in particular to prevent them eating unnecessary food and snacks.

A number of people suffer from taking small snacks during the day and hence over-eat, whether or not they consume low-calorie items at meal times. Very often this act is done almost subconsciously. The present invention provides an alarm which activates itself when the hand of a person approaches their mouth, so as to remind and educate themselves that they should not be eating snacks and the like.

According to the invention there is provided a device for attachment to the arm of a person, said device comprising an alarm and an alarm activator, said alarm activator being adapted to activate the alarm when the lower arm is in the vertical or near-vertical position when the hand places an item of food in the mouth. Preferably the device is in the form of a bracelet worn on the lower arm around the wrist. Further modifications will be apparent to those skilled in the art.

In use, as the alarm is activated every time the wearer tries to eat, it makes them think about their action and reminds them not to eat.

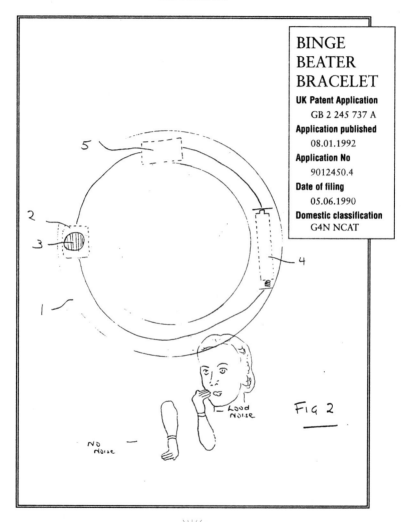

BINGE BEATER BRACELET

UK Patent Application
GB 2 245 737 A

Application published
08.01.1992

Application No
9012450.4

Date of filing
05.06.1990

Domestic classification
G4N NCAT

FIG 2

A TOOTHBRUSH

UK Patent Application

GB 2 243 072 A

Application published

23.10.1991

Application No

9108686.8

Date of filing

19.04.1991

Domestic classification

A4K KFX

UIS SII25

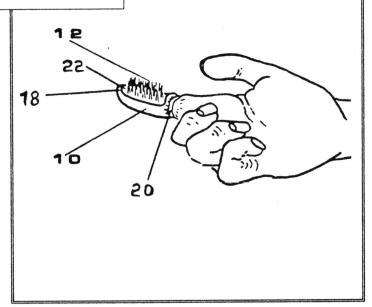

A Toothbrush

The present invention relates to a novel form of toothbrush.

A conventional toothbrush comprises a rigid handle and head and an elongated rigid item such as this is not easily carried around for casual use. When carried in a pocket, a conventional toothbrush is liable to distort the clothing of the person carrying it and/or may be a source of discomfort. However, a toothbrush may occupy valuable space if carried in a handbag, briefcase or other such bag. In addition, a toothbrush which is wet after use is an inconvenient article to carry. For these reasons, although sound practice requires regular brushing of the teeth, few people take the bother to brush their teeth as often as dentists recommend.

It is an object ot the present invention to overcome or reduce the foregoing inconveniences by providing a toothbrush which is conveniently portable.

The toothbrush according to the present invention comprises a sleeve to fit over a finger-end and a number of bristles extending from an outer surface of the sleeve, as can readily be recognised, when the sleeve of this novel toothbrush is fitted upon a finger, it is able to function in the same manner as a conventional toothbrush, while at the same time being sufficiently compact for convenient carrying in the pocket or elsewhere until it is required for use.

Educational Gloves

This invention relates to gloves, and particularly to gloves which provide a technical interaction with the wearer.

It is well established that the human brain commits to memory items of information more readily if that information is presented to it more than just once. Frequent reinforcement greatly assists retention of the information.

I have appreciated that one very commom retention problem can be facilitated by the use of special gloves. In these gloves, different information is located on different fingers (which term as used herein conveniently includes the thumb). Furthermore, the retention is facilitated by specially structuring the information in relation to the individual fingers.

Each glove is designed to facilitate retention in the wearer's brain (usually a child's) of one multiplication table. The gloves respectively cover the two times to ten times tables, but could of course be extended. The gloves are thus as good as a computerised multiplication teaching system, with the added advantage that the reinforcing effect is not confined to special times when the system is used, but is available whenever the gloves are worn. What is more, they keep the user warm.

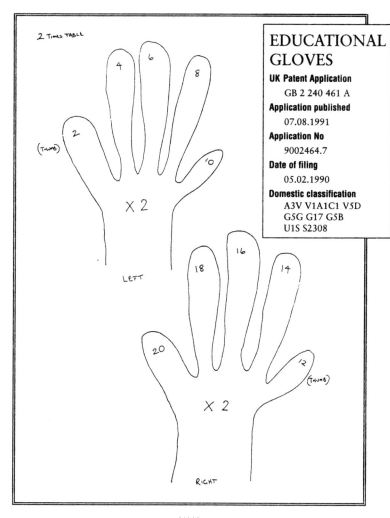

2 TIMES TABLE

(THUMB) 2
4
6
8
10

X 2

LEFT

18
16
14
20
12 (THUMB)

X 2

RIGHT

EDUCATIONAL GLOVES

UK Patent Application

GB 2 240 461 A

Application published

07.08.1991

Application No

9002464.7

Date of filing

05.02.1990

Domestic classification

A3V V1A1C1 V5D
G5G G17 G5B
U1S S2308

ANIMAL FAECES COLLECTOR

UK Patent Application

GB 2 238 454 A

Application published

05.06.1991

Application No

9024634.9

Date of filing

13.11.1990

Domestic classification

A1M MCJ

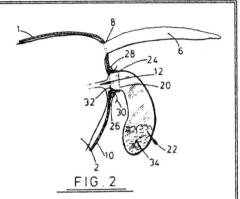

FIG. 2

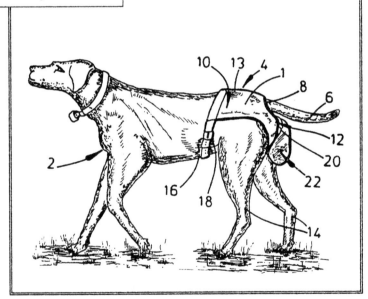

Animal Faeces Collector

Animals are in general not particular about where they defecate. The streets, parks and pavements of our towns everywhere are littered with, especially, dog excreta. It is unsightly, unhygenic, inconvenient and in the case of canine animals can harbour dangerous diseases such as toxocara which affects humans. Additionally owners who leave their animals at home when they are out often return to find soiled carpets.

The collector comprises a harness (10) mounting a generally anular connector means (26) defining a passage (20) for excrement (34) therethrough. The harness (10) is formed and arranged for releasable attachment to said animal's hind section with said passage (20) substantially directly opposite and adjacent said animal's anal orifice (12). The connector (26) is formed and arranged for releasable engagement with the mouth (30) of an animal excreta-receiving container (22) and being provided with releasable securing means for captively retaining said container (22) in engagement with the connector (26) in use of the collector (1), such that faeces (34) excreted by said animal whilst in the defecating position can pass through the passage (20) in the anular connector section (26) into the excreta-receiving container (22).

Anal Wiping Implement

Particularly elderly people find it difficult, after emptying their bowels on a toilet, to hold the toilet paper in one hand and by twisting their body to wipe themselves properly from the backside between their buttocks. The present invention comprises an improvement by means of which no twisting of body occurs and yet the wiping is made easier and more efficient and in a more hygienic way.

In order that the invention may be more readily understood, it will be described by way of an example, with reference to the accompanying drawing wherein:

➤ Fig.1 shows a person just leaving the toilet seat and holding in one hand the invention to be used to wipe himself between said person's legs.

➤ Fig.2 shows inter alia the end tip of the invention touching the person's anus so as to accomplish the wiping off.

➤ Fig.3 shows the position in which the person will have to hold the invention as shown in Fig.1.

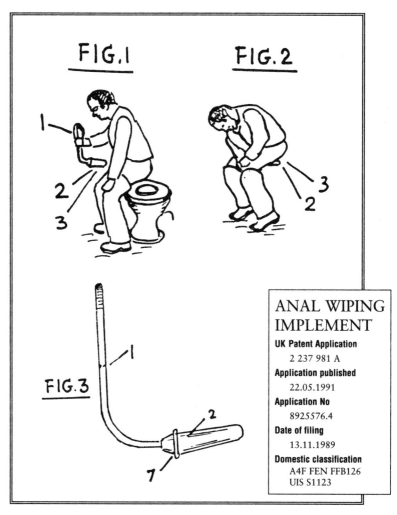

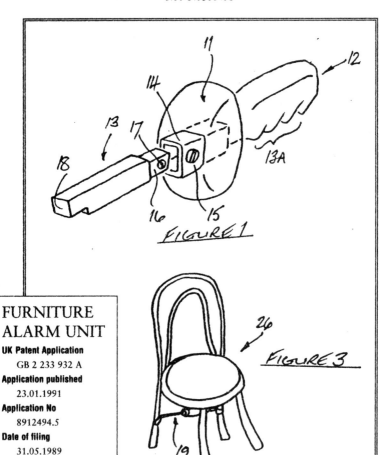

FIGURE 1

FIGURE 3

FURNITURE ALARM UNIT

UK Patent Application
GB 2 233 932 A

Application published
23.01.1991

Application No
8912494.5

Date of filing
31.05.1989

Domestic classification
B5L LF
A41 LAAL L144

Furniture Alarm Unit

The inventive concept is concerned with two inventions, a woodworker's push-stick and a furniture alarm unit.

Such an alarm unit is particularly applicable to, for example, antique chairs which are all too often tilted backwards, unthinkingly, by their occupant who leans back in the chair and effectively levers the chair about its back legs. Quite apart from the fact that the chairs were not intended for such use, the costs nowadays of stripping and repairing a chair whose joints have become loosened can be high.

Such costs are certainly out of all proportion to the minor thought and effort needed to avoid the problem in the first place. But human nature being what it is, the problem will persist unless there is some immediate, effective and if necessary initially rather startling warning. An alarm unit embodying this aspect of the inventive concept provides such a warning.

When the chair is tilted backwards (i.e. when it is levered about its back legs) beyond a predetermined amount, the alarm is activated.

The result is to warn, indeed to startle, the occupant of the chair. The long-term effect is to dissuade him from doing it again.

A Combination Backpack, Camp-bed and Frame Tent

Backpacking has become an ever more popular pastime, and has been promoted by improvements in equipment. However, when backpacking, it is not usually possible also to carry a camp-bed which will enable the user to obtain a comfortable and undisturbed night's sleep.

Equipment for backpackers is usually rugged and primitive, and it is considered normal for individuals to sleep on the ground with nothing more than a waterproof groundsheet for protection. The present invention seeks to provide a combined unit which will obviate many of these disadvantages and enable individuals to carry with them, on their backs, a much greater range of useful equipment than has hithertofore been possible, allowing backpackers to extend the range of their activities.

The present invention relates generally to a combination backpack, camp-bed and frame tent, and to a structure formed as a combination of any two of these, namely a combination backpack and frame tent, a combination backpack and camp-bed, or a combination frame tent and camp-bed.

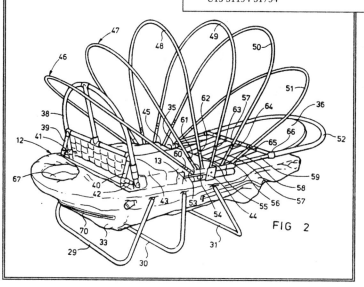

A COMBINATION BACKPACK, CAMP-BED AND FRAME TENT

UK Patent Application

GB 2 228 191 A

Application published

22.08.1990

Application No

9003884.5

Date of filing

21.02.1990

Domestic classification

A4L LAAB L105 L107 A4G G7
E1D DF157 DGS2 D2019
U1S S1154 S1734

FIG 2

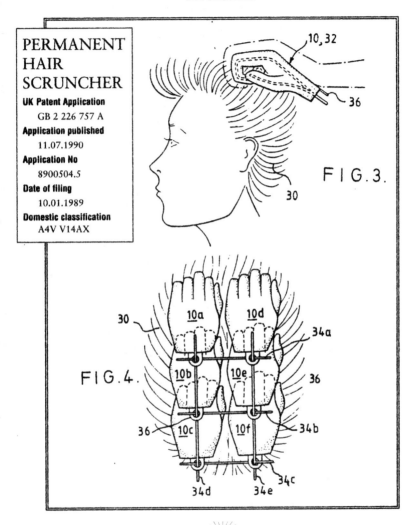

PERMANENT HAIR SCRUNCHER

UK Patent Application
GB 2 226 757 A

Application published
11.07.1990

Application No
8900504.5

Date of filing
10.01.1989

Domestic classification
A4V V14AX

FIG.3.

FIG.4.

Permanent Hair Scruncher

This invention relates to the permanent-waving of hair.

Modern styles of permanent-waving of hair often require the hair not to be curled, but to be 'scrunched'.

Referring to Fig. 3, the human hand is used initially to 'scrunch' the lady's hair (30) and is then replaced by the artificial hand (10), which is applied to the lady's hair (30) opened-out and is then closed tightly into a fist (32), as shown, holding a fistful of hair (not visible) tightly 'scrunched-up'. This can be held for the duration of the development time of the lotion (typically half-an-hour to one hour).

Referring to Fig. 4, several such artificial hands (10a–f) are applied to the hair in square areas of the head in this way, one-by-one, after the hair has been scrunched in each square area by the human hand, prior to the application of a standard permanent-waving lotion. It is important that no hair (30) remains 'unscrunched'.

For a lady with short hair, the effect may be to give 'body' to the hair without curling it and to give a tousled or 'scrunched' appearance to the hair. For medium-length or long hair the effect may be to provide a 'grown-out' or shaggy appearance, which may also be described as 'scrunched'. In any event curling the hair can be avoided.

Adjustable Inflatable Headband

This invention relates to an adjustable inflatable headband.

This, when inflated by air or helium and worn around the head, increases blood flow generally to the scalp. This effect is due to the reduction of scalp tension and the resultant increase in scalp mobility. This is a simple, novel and mechanical method and apparatus to reactivate dormant hair follicles. It will improve the condition of existing hair, as well as stimulating new hair growth.

It is adjustable for size by means of friction pads at each end. Friction pads on the exterior surface allow the fixing of aesthetic extras such as hats, wigs, and decorative materials. The apparatus may be in various colours incorporated either in or on the materials of construction.

The typically balding male dons the headband part of the apparatus above the ears and below the scalp. By means of the hand bulb or a helium cannister, the headband is inflated through the two-way preset valves to a comfortable pressure.

The aesthetic coverings may be donned with no loss of effectiveness.

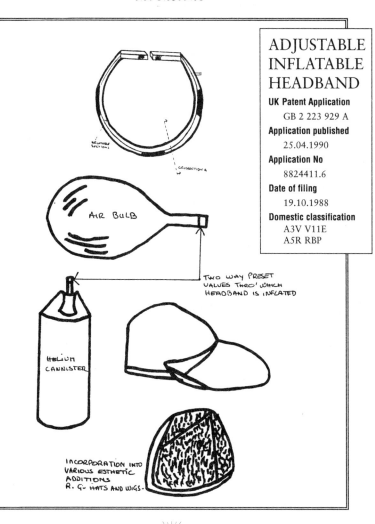

ADJUSTABLE
INFLATABLE
HEADBAND

UK Patent Application
GB 2 223 929 A

Application published
25.04.1990

Application No
8824411.6

Date of filing
19.10.1988

Domestic classification
A3V V11E
A5R RBP

INFLATABLE
SECTIONS

CROSSECTION A

AIR BULB

TWO WAY PRESET
VALVES THRO' WHICH
HEADBAND IS INFLATED

HELIUM
CANNISTER

INCORPORATION INTO
VARIOUS ESTHETIC
ADDITIONS
R. G. HATS AND WIGS.

IMPROVED GLOVES AND MITTENS

UK Patent Application

GB 2 221 607 A

Application published

14.02.1990

Application No

8907861.2

Date of filing

07.04.1989

Domestic classification

A3V V1A1C1 V1A1C2

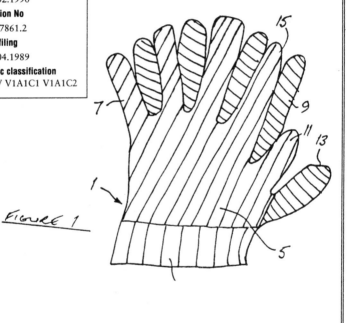

FIGURE 1

Improved Gloves and Mittens

In cold weather, if a couple who are wearing gloves wish to hold hands, they have the options of keeping their gloves on, in which case there is no contact between the hands, or they can remove the gloves or mittens and hold hands directly, in which case the hands will get cold. This is unsatisfactory and indeed unromantic.

According to the invention there is provided a garment for wear on the hands, intended to accommodate two hands, the garment including an opening through which the hands may pass into the main body of the garment, and projecting from the main body of the garment two finger receiving areas, each finger receiving area being capable of receiving the fingers of a respective hand, and two thumb receiving areas, each thumb receiving area being capable of receiving a thumb of a respective hand, the finger receiving areas being separate from one another such that two hands within the garment are positioned with their palms in contact in the main body of the garment with their respective fingers in the finger receiving areas, allowing free movement of the digits.

The garment therefore can be worn by two people walking along hand-in-hand so that their palms are kept in contact but their hands are kept warm.

Dancing Shoes

The present invention relates to dancing shoes.

One of the skills required from a dancer is to control body and limbs in flowing movements which overcome also the impediment of friction at the interface between the feet and the ground.

However, even with sophisticated surfaces, the rotation of a dancer supported on his foot or feet remains comparatively restricted. For this reason, to distribute the impediment, a rotation is generally executed in a number of space-consuming steps or, where on modern dance floors, space was confined, 'crush' or 'rhythm' dancing – albeit with impoverished vitality – became the vogue.

It is an object of the present invention to provide a dancing shoe which allows the dancer to rotate freely on any normal dance floor without in any way limiting customary movements or departing from the customary appearance of modern dancers. New movements are made possible: rotation, either on heel or toe, and longitudinal movement in a straight line or curve by placing the body-weight over selected edges of each shoe. The shoes should therefore appeal to the amateur as well as to those, all over the world who, dedicated to excel, will be able to develop an exciting new dance form.

The shoes may further be embellished with attachments which, by rotation, generate sound effects or sparks issuing from underneath.

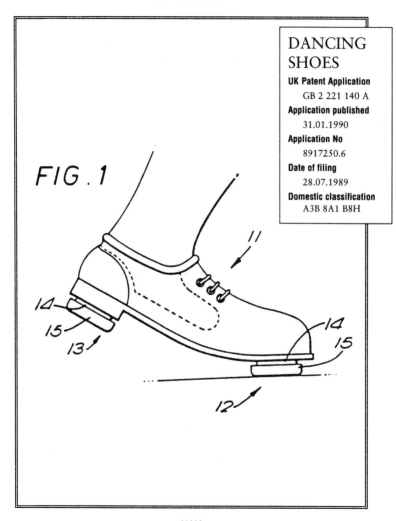

FIG . 1

DANCING SHOES

UK Patent Application
GB 2 221 140 A
Application published
31.01.1990
Application No
8917250.6
Date of filing
28.07.1989
Domestic classification
A3B 8A1 B8H

A SPROOSSER

UK Patent Application

GB 2 204 228 A

Application published

09.11.1988

Application No

8709768

Date of filing

24.04.1987

Domestic classification

A4F EK31 FBH
B2E 1544 1739 1747 404S
553T 556T 600T KD
U1S 1138 1149

FIG.1a.

FIG.2.

FIG.3.

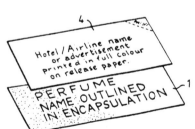

Hotel / Airline name
or advertisement
printed in full colour
on release paper.

PERFUME
NAME OUTLINED
IN ENCAPSULATION

FIG.4.

A Sproosser

Device for Cleaning Clothing

This invention relates to a cleaning device for the removal of foreign matter from the surface of clothing or cloth.

It is an object of this invention to provide a cleaning device particularly suitable for removing detritus deposited by the body on clothing. It is inevitable in the physiology of human beings that every person sheds skin and hair. According to this invention there is provided a cleaning device comprising a paper or cardboard base, a layer formed on the base made up of a plurality of first cells and a plurality of second cells, said first cells being of adhesive material, said second cells being of perfumed material, and a release paper which covers the layer.

In use, the release paper is peeled off, revealing the layer of first and second cells on the base. The base with its layer is then stroked over clothing, for example, a collar or cloth surface, and the adhesive material gathers up any human detritus or dust; the human detritus can be expected to be hairs, dead skin or the like. The perfumed material can be arranged to be similar to an aftershave and could counteract the effect of tobacco, for example.

The cleaning device may be utilised to carry advertising material.

Information Wristband

The present invention relates to information wristbands. More particularly, but not exclusively, it relates to information wristbands of the type in which the information can be easily updated if that should be required.

One method of storing information presently known is a pocket diary. This suffers from the disadvantages that it is bulky, and not always easy to obtain immediate access. Another method of storing information is a scrap of paper or the back of an envelope, in which case the problems which may arise are those of locating the information when it is required or sometimes at all.

According to the present invention there is provided a wristband comprising an inner band and a transparent outer band, one edge being openable and at least one sheet of paper insertable through said open edge.

The apparatus of the invention has a number of uses. As well as diary function and daily appointment function, the information contained within the wristband may represent a workman's work schedule, a housewife's shopping list, the notes of a speech maker, the round of a delivery man, or it may serve a simple routine-keeping function.

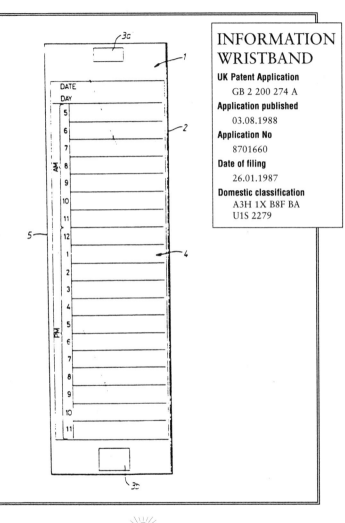

INFORMATION WRISTBAND

UK Patent Application

GB 2 200 274 A

Application published

03.08.1988

Application No

8701660

Date of filing

26.01.1987

Domestic classification

A3H 1X B8F BA
U1S 2279

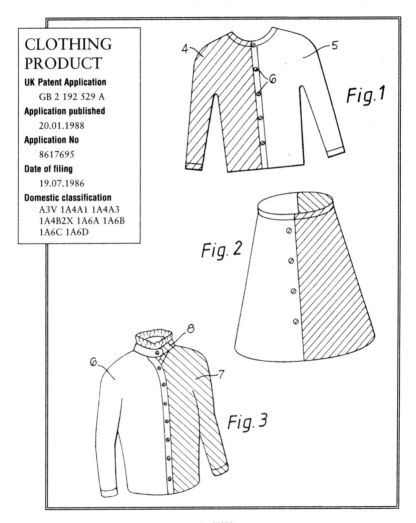

CLOTHING PRODUCT

UK Patent Application
GB 2 192 529 A

Application published
20.01.1988

Application No
8617695

Date of filing
19.07.1986

Domestic classification
A3V 1A4A1 1A4A3
1A4B2X 1A6A 1A6B
1A6C 1A6D

Fig.1

Fig. 2

Fig. 3

Clothing Product

The present invention is a clothing product of a novel type, devised to permit a person the opportunity to vary the appearance of a garment with considerations of fashion and novelty in mind.

Most individuals have favourite garments, reflecting a particular aspect of the wearer's taste in terms of style or comfort. However, the natural desire for change of appearance may discourage the wearer from wearing that same favourite garment on too many occasions. It is therefore an object of the present invention to provide a clothing product which allows the user greater flexibility in influencing and modifying the appearance of a garment.

The clothing product according to the present invention comprises half a complete garment, not forming a complete item of clothing in itself. It is the main intention that two half garments which are removably attached to each other should be visually distinguished from each other in order to produce an interesting fashion effect. By detaching the halves and replacing one of them the effect can be markedly changed. In ringing the changes, the wearer may sometimes choose to combine two halves which do not contrast at all.

Feeding Spoon

This invention relates to feeding spoons, and is particularly although not exclusively concerned with spoons that may be used for weaning infants.

As many mothers will know, teaching young babies to eat from a spoon can be a messy business. We have noticed that when most young babies begin to be spoon fed, they tend to pull down their chins to their chests, which makes feeding both difficult and messy. We aim to improve upon this situation, by providing a feeding spoon which may counteract this tendency.

According to one aspect of the present invention, there is provided a feeding spoon comprising a bowl and a handle and, extending upwardly from the handle, an extension which carries attraction means for attracting the attention of an infant being fed with the spoon. Preferably, the attraction means makes a sound when the spoon is moved – for example, in the manner of a rattle.

We have found that, when an infant is attracted by the attraction means, it may lift its head in an inquisitive manner, but not its lower jaw, such that the mouth is left open to accept food.

It will be appreciated that, not only does the illustrated spoon (1) serve a purpose as an improved feeding spoon, it may also serve as an interesting toy and rattle for a child, as it grows older.

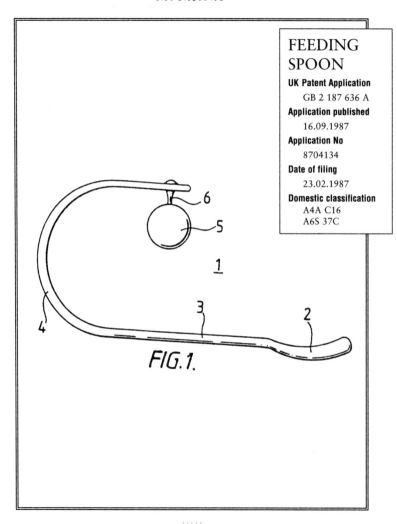

FEEDING
SPOON

UK Patent Application
GB 2 187 636 A

Application published
16.09.1987

Application No
8704134

Date of filing
23.02.1987

Domestic classification
A4A C16
A6S 37C

FIG.1.

WALKING AIDS

UK Patent Application

   GB 2 184 651 A

Application published

   01.07.1987

Application No

   8629262

Date of filing

   08.12.1986

Domestic classification

   A4P 1315 22D 22L
   A6D 35D

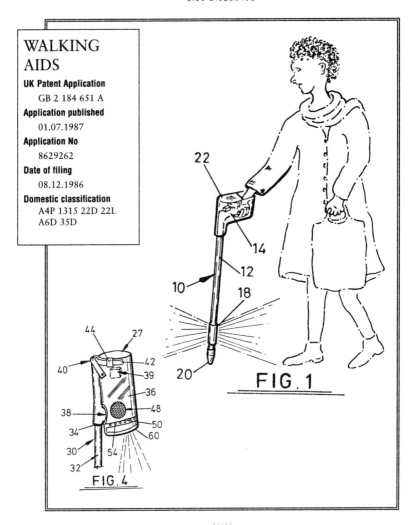

FIG. 1

FIG. 4

Walking Aids

This invention concerns walking aids such as walking-sticks and crutches but may also be applicable to skiing poles.

Users of walking aids are normally the old, the disabled and generally the infirm who despite their disabilities have to venture into the world outside their homes for one reason or another.

Consequently every passing day brings news of elderly or handicapped persons being knocked down and seriously injured or killed. Another danger that the old, most of whom are walking aid users, tend to be exposed to is robbery with violence, many-a-time at their front doors. Many walking aid users are often unable to gain access quickly enough into their homes because they spend a long time fumbling for the right door keys with partially frozen fingers. This is when they are often preyed upon by opportunist muggers.

According to the invention there is provided a walking aid comprising a stick or crutch having associated therewith a light source and a glove or pocket about the grippable part of the stick.

In time it is hoped that the walking aid of the invention will come to be identified with the old and infirm and consequently viewed as an invitation for help and care whenever deemed necessary by the more able-bodied members of the public, including motor vehicle drivers when this time comes.

A Shopping List Holder

This invention relates to a shopping list holder.

Shopping lists are often made up on scraps of paper. The scraps of paper are in a variety of shapes and sizes and they often become mislaid or totally lost. Directly this happens, they cease to be useful and the owner of the shopping list is left wondering exactly what was on the shopping list.

It is an aim of the present invention to help to at least partially alleviate the above-mentioned problem.

Accordingly, this invention provides a shopping list holder comprising a flat container that has a front face, an opposing face, one open edge defining a mouth for insertion of a shopping list, three closed sides, and an aperture in the front face, at least the front face being made of a transparent plastic material.

The shopping list holder may include attachment means for attaching it to a desired object, for example a shopping bag, a handbag, a shopping trolley or a user's wrist.

The shopping list holder may be sold with or without at least one piece of paper positioned in the container. It is envisaged that the shopping list holder will be sold with a separate pad of pieces of paper for acting as shopping lists.

The pad of the pieces of paper may advantageously be headed with the words 'shopping list'.

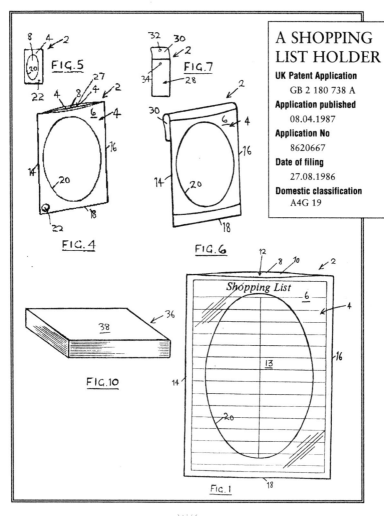

A SHOPPING LIST HOLDER

UK Patent Application

GB 2 180 738 A

Application published

08.04.1987

Application No

8620667

Date of filing

27.08.1986

Domestic classification

A4G 19

FIG.5

FIG.7

FIG.4

FIG.6

FIG.10

Shopping List

FIG.1

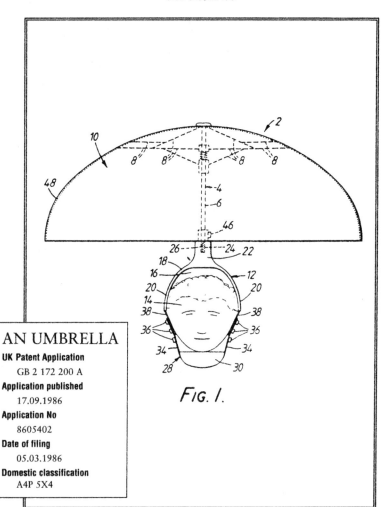

AN UMBRELLA

UK Patent Application

GB 2 172 200 A

Application published

17.09.1986

Application No

8605402

Date of filing

05.03.1986

Domestic classification

A4P 5X4

FIG. 1.

An Umbrella

This invention relates to an umbrella.

Umbrellas are well-known and they have a frame which is covered by material. The known umbrellas suffer from the considerable disadvantage that, when the frame is in its unfolded protecting position, the umbrella has to be held above a person's head by the person holding the rod with one hand. Thus, one hand of the person is constantly engaged and this often causes inconvenience and difficulty in that the person cannot easily perform other everyday tasks such for example as holding shopping bags and cases and/or getting out money to purchase things.

It is an aim of the present invention to obviate or reduce the above-mentioned problems of the known umbrellas.

Accordingly, this invention provides an umbrella comprising a frame for supporting the umbrella frame on a person's head.

Especially with women, it is not generally acceptable for their hair to be messed up or disarranged. The umbrella of the present invention can be used for its desired purposes without messing up the person's hair. This is because the frame support means is such that it supports the umbrella frame on the person's head such that the frame support means is positioned above and spaced apart from the person's head.

The umbrella of the present invention can be used for all of the uses that existing umbrellas are currently used for.

Improvements in Toothbrushes

This invention relates to toothbrushes.

It has been found that biting a relatively soft material has a beneficial effect on the teeth and gums. However, the material from which conventional toothbrushes is made has been found to be too hard for biting purposes. The material should be much softer and preferably slightly resilient. However, a toothbrush cannot be made of such material because the handle would then be too flexible when the toothbrush was being used for brushing the teeth in a conventional manner. On the other hand a totally independent article solely for biting is likely to encounter consumer resistance.

The present invention aims to provide a toothbrush which overcomes these problems.

According to the invention, there is provided a toothbrush wherein at least a portion of the handle is provided with a layer of relatively soft material which is adpated to be bitten. Said layer of relatively soft material takes the form of a sleeve fitted over said portion of the handle. This permits sleeves of different hardnesses to be fitted on the toothbrush so that a user can progress, for example, from a very soft material to progressively harder material as his teeth become stronger from biting.

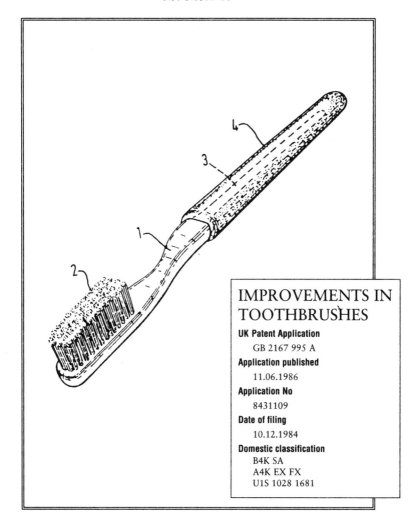

IMPROVEMENTS IN TOOTHBRUSHES

UK Patent Application

GB 2167 995 A

Application published

11.06.1986

Application No

8431109

Date of filing

10.12.1984

Domestic classification

B4K SA
A4K EX FX
U1S 1028 1681

MULTI-PURPOSE COAT

UK Patent Application

GB 2 163 942 A

Application published

12.03.1986

Application No

8521653

Date of filing

30.08.1985

Domestic classification

A3V 1A6G 1A6H 45R
6D1 6D2

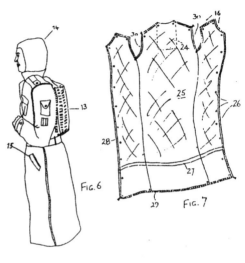

Fig. 6

Fig. 7

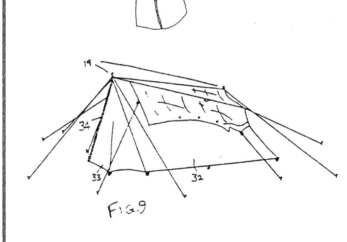

FIG. 9

Multi-purpose Coat

This invention relates to a waterproof coat which includes, or is combined with, other features or elements of use for camping or sleeping.

Broadly stated the invention consists of a coat formed with attached or removable elements capable of forming a tent, and/or sleeping-bag, and/or rucksack. In one preferred design the coat has a detachable padded lining provided with closure means to form a sleeping-bag. The coat may also be permanently or detachably connected to tent sections which have means to hold them folded inside the coat, or opened out to form the tent. The coat itself conveniently forms part of the tent surface thus reducing overall weight and the arms of the coat are for this purpose provided with zip closures adjacent to the armholes.

The tent sections preferably include locating eyes for tent pegs, tent ropes and guy ropes, and a zip-closed opening for the tent, and the coat may have a pocket or other compartment for a sectional tent pole.

According to another preferred feature of the invention, the coat has an external built-in or removable pack or rucksack and it may have a pocket receiving a waterproof hood.

Book Rests

This invention relates to rests, holders or like support devices for a book, document or like item to be read or otherwise viewed.

The inventor has appreciated that ordinary book rests and the like are not suitable for people who are lying on their backs, who find it very tiring or impossible to hold a book in a convenient position for them to read it.

The invention consists of a rest, holder or support device. The advantage is that the viewer can view the book etc. from a supine position, with their head facing upwards and not to the side, without having to hold the book etc. above them.

A particularly convenient form of the device for outdoor use or use when there is no bed headboard available is obtained if the device is made of bridge form. In this case, said support means may for convenience and ease of manufacture, together with cheapness, comprise two opposite side supports for said member which are substantially of sheet form. If one or both of said side supports comprise a substantial transparent area, this will allow viewing there-through of the viewer's surroundings which may have psychological and other advantages, and will facilitate illumination there-through of the book etc.

BOOK RESTS

UK Patent Application
GB 2 150 018 A

Application published
26.06.1985

Application No
8330963

Date of filing
19.11.1983

Domestic classification
A4L 118 307 ABA

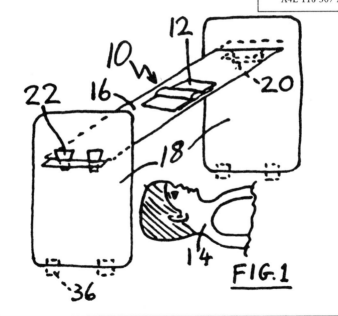

FIG.1

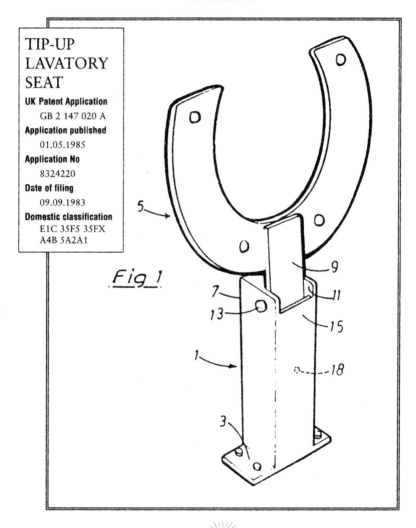

TIP-UP LAVATORY SEAT

UK Patent Application
GB 2 147 020 A

Application published
01.05.1985

Application No
8324220

Date of filing
09.09.1983

Domestic classification
E1C 35F5 35FX
A4B 5A2A1

Fig_1

Tip-up Lavatory Seat

The present invention relates to a sanitary fitment for use in lavatories.

In numerous foreign lavatories an aperture is merely provided in the ground and a person has to crouch over this aperture. It is, however, difficult for the old and infirm to attain and maintain this crouched position.

The aim of the present invention is to provide a universal sanitary fitment which modifies such primitive toilet facilities, making it easier for persons to use the facility.

Thus, by virtue of the present invention the curved seat member can be pivoted to the generally horizontal position to allow a person to be supported above the lavatory aperture, the horse-shoe-shaped preferred embodiment being suitable for easy use by either male or female.

Advantageously, the support can carry one or more nozzles for directing a water jet or jets upwardly towards the user in the manner of a bidet. For this purpose, each nozzle is adapted to be connected to a hot and/or cold water supply via pipework containing a valve controllable by means of a suitable actuating device, such as a lever or push-button.

Preferably, the seat member is formed of cold pressed steel covered with a plastics material.

Undergarment with Pockets

The invention relates to men's or women's pants, panties, boxer shorts, knickers and like undergarments having a waistband, and is characterised in that at least one pocket is provided adjacent to the waistband at the front or back of the garment. The garment is preferably made of jersey or similar stretch material with an elasticated waistband and dimensioned to fit snugly to the wearer.

The upper edge of each pocket is open and is reinforced or decorated with an edging of lace or other suitable and relatively inextensible material. When the garment is being worn (Figure 3) the edging is extended, pulling out the folds so that it and the pocket lie snugly against the wearer reducing the possibility of the pockets forming undesirable and tell-tale bumpy patterns on the outer garment.

The pockets are conveniently dimensioned for carrying paper money, avoiding loss by bag-snatching and pocket-picking. It is more comfortable and convenient to wear than a wallet belt. Further, the invention can be applied to men's undergarments such as Y-front pants which can conveniently be made of cotton jersey.

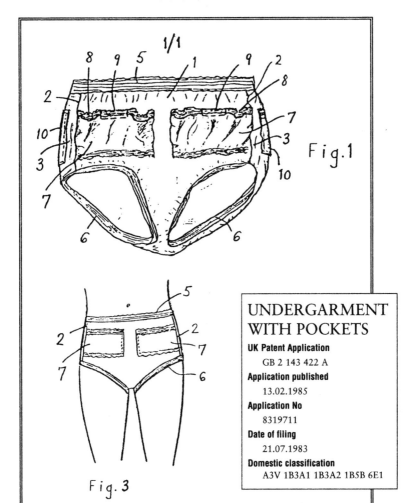

1/1

Fig.1

Fig.3

UNDERGARMENT WITH POCKETS

UK Patent Application

GB 2 143 422 A

Application published

13.02.1985

Application No

8319711

Date of filing

21.07.1983

Domestic classification

A3V 1B3A1 1B3A2 1B5B 6E1

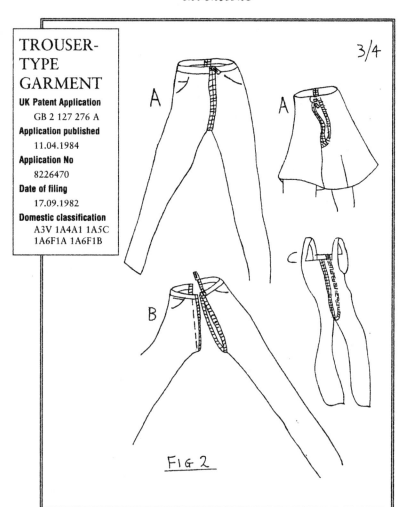

TROUSER-TYPE GARMENT

UK Patent Application

GB 2 127 276 A

Application published

11.04.1984

Application No

8226470

Date of filing

17.09.1982

Domestic classification

A3V 1A4A1 1A5C
1A6F1A 1A6F1B

FIG 2

Trouser-type Garment

This invention relates to a trouser-type garment that separates into two or more separate pieces. By 'trouser-type garment' we include not only short and long trousers, but also any garments designed for wear around the abdomen and crotch, e.g. swimsuits, briefs etc.

A person wearing said garment may gain access to the genital and anal areas without necessitating complete removal or lowering of the said garment. This makes urination, defecation, copulation, and access to genital and anal areas possible without removal or lowering said garment.

The users will find ease during use of lavatories where complete removal or lowering of clothing is not desired. Users who need more frequent use of lavatory i.e. pregnant women and sick people, will also find use of this garment beneficial. Those needing to urinate or defecate during outdoor activities where public conveniences are not within reach and removing or lowering of clothing is not desired will find said garment an advantage. Outdoor and industrial worktime may be considerably shortened when said invention is implemented. In children's wear, for changing of underwear, cleaning, defecation, urination, this type of garment will save time and be more convenient.

The Whoopsy Bag

Use: To clear away solids hygienically.

Background: At present one has to use two separate items, namely a shovel and a bag.

General Description: The Whoopsy Bag is a scraper attached to the base of a bag.

Detailed Desription: To use the Whoopsy Bag the hand is put inside the bag and grips the attached scraper. The scraper is then pushed under the unwanted material and picks it up. The bag is then pulled inside out over the scraper, sealed and thrown away.

Exploitation:
Whoopsy Bags in the Home. They are ideal for clearing up spilt food, sickness or animal faeces.
Whoopsy Bags in the Car/ on the Boat/ in the Plane. Car sickness, sea sickness and air sickness quickly and hygienically cleared away using a Whoopsy Bag.
Whoopsy Bags on the Footpath/Recreation Ground. Animal faeces quickly and hygienically cleared up from paths, play areas and shoes.

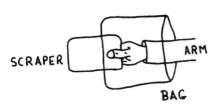

SCRAPER ARM

BAG

Fig1 : Plan View

THE WHOOPSY BAG

UK Patent Application
GB 2 100 581 A

Application published
22.08.1982

Application No
8118868

Date of filing
06.01.1981

Domestic classification
A4A E8

SCRAPER ARM

BAG

Fig2: Elevation

BIN

(i) Approach (ii) Pick-Up (iii) Disposal

Fig3: Actions

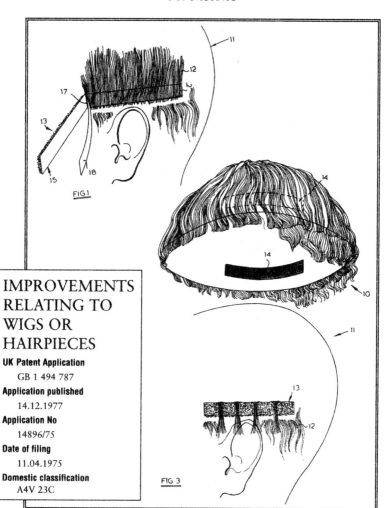

IMPROVEMENTS RELATING TO WIGS OR HAIRPIECES

UK Patent Application

GB 1 494 787

Application published

14.12.1977

Application No

14896/75

Date of filing

11.04.1975

Domestic classification

A4V 23C

FIG 1

FIG 3

Improvements Relating to Wigs or Hairpieces and Method of Attachment

This invention relates to a wig or hairpiece and its method of attachment to the head. The expression 'hairpiece' is used hereinafter in a generic sense as meaning either a complete wig which simulates a whole head of hair or a smaller piece which simulates only part of a head of hair.

One method of attachment now being practised is where some of the remaining natural hair is plaited to form a 'rope' extending from one side of the head around the back to the other side. The peripheral edge of the hairpiece is then anchored to this rope of natural hair by a stitching operation. This method does have certain drawbacks. Due to the normal growth of the natural hair remaining on the head, the connection between the hair and the hairpiece will tend to loosen over a period of time. Also, during the wearing of such a hairpiece, if it becomes necessary for the wearer to attend to the scalp for cleaning or other purposes again it is necessary for the specialist to be visited in order for the hairpiece to be removed and then replaced.

According to one aspect of the invention I provide a method of attaching a hairpiece to a head having some existing hair and using a two part fastener of the type which is presently known under the name of 'Velcro' (registered Trade Mark).

Weatherproof Garment

This invention relates to a weatherproof garment for covering the whole of the upper part of the body and which is readily portable when not in use.

According to the invention a weatherproof garment is designed to be suspended from, and supported by, the head of the wearer. When worn the garment is preferably conical in shape, the conical shape giving a wide base to the garment, which can then accommodate a collapsible stool to enable the wearer to sit inside the garment. Shapes other than conical are of course possible and the garment may be cylindrical with a circular, elliptical, square or other cross-section.

The garment should have a visor of clear material, but the remainder of the flexible material may be of any required pattern or colour. The garment can be particularly useful for watching sporting events, and also for activities such as angling and bird-watching. In the case of bird-watching the material of the garment can be designed to have a camouflaging effect so that the garment can blend with the countryside and act as a portable hide. The garment may have a front flap which is open for angling.

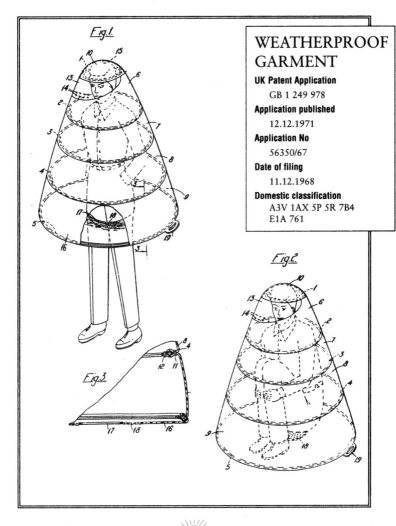

Fig.1.

WEATHERPROOF GARMENT

UK Patent Application
GB 1 249 978

Application published
12.12.1971

Application No
56350/67

Date of filing
11.12.1968

Domestic classification
A3V 1AX 5P 5R 7B4
E1A 761

Fig.2

Fig.3

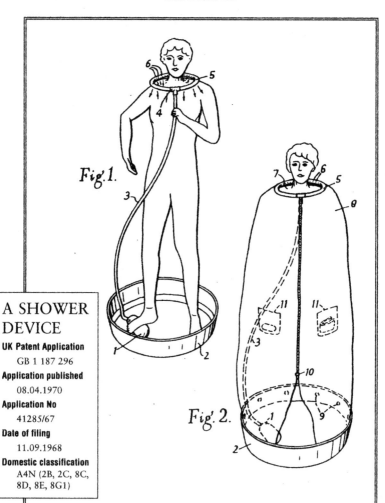

Fig. 1.

Fig. 2.

A SHOWER DEVICE

UK Patent Application
   GB 1 187 296

Application published
   08.04.1970

Application No
   41285/67

Date of filing
   11.09.1968

Domestic classification
   A4N (2B, 2C, 8C, 8D, 8E, 8G1)

A Shower Device

This invention relates to shower means for personal bathing, its object being to provide an improved construction of shower device which permits, inter alia, (i) the direction of liquid onto the body so as to avoid splashing, (ii) the recirculation of a relatively small quantity of liquid.

According to the present invention, a shower device comprises a ring of tubular material adapted to allow passage of the head and neck of the user but adapted to rest on the shoulders, said ring having jet-forming perforations on its internal periphery to direct jets of liquid inwardly by means of a foot operated pump.

Such a device can be operated with the user standing or seated in a container holding a relatively small quantity of water which is recirculated by the foot pump as often as required. To accommodate soap, a flannel, or a towel, the enclosure may have one or more pockets on its internal surface.

Improvements in Neckware

This invention concerns neckwear, principally ties. According to the invention I provide neckwear, such as a tie, having a pad or cloth attached to its rear, at or near one end, for use in cleaning the lenses of spectacles.

It is well-known that spectacle lenses require frequent cleaning. Cloths and tissues can be obtained for this purpose, but these can be mislaid and not available when required. Cleaning cloths are available for retention in a spectacle case, and even if the case is being carried by a person it is necessary for this to be taken generally from a pocket and opened to obtain the cloth.

By providing a cleaning pad or cloth combined with a tie, in accordance with this invention, there is always available and at hand to a person wearing such a tie a means for cleaning and polishing spectacle lenses, especially when seated at a desk or in a chair.

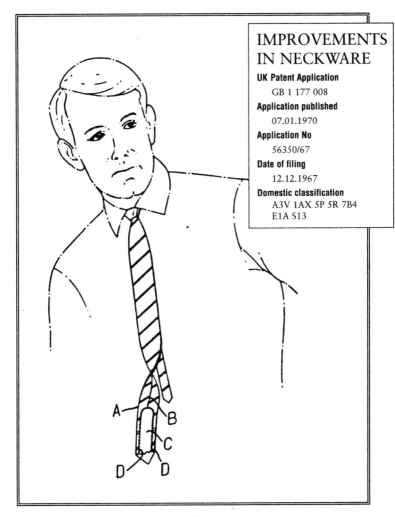

IMPROVEMENTS IN NECKWARE

UK Patent Application
GB 1 177 008

Application published
07.01.1970

Application No
56350/67

Date of filing
12.12.1967

Domestic classification
A3V 1AX 5P 5R 7B4
E1A S13

IMPROVEMENTS IN GARMENTS

UK Patent Application

GB 1 072 274

Application published

14.06.1967

Application No

4268/65

Date of filing

22.02.1966

Domestic classification

A3V (1 A6X4)

A4 G10

S13

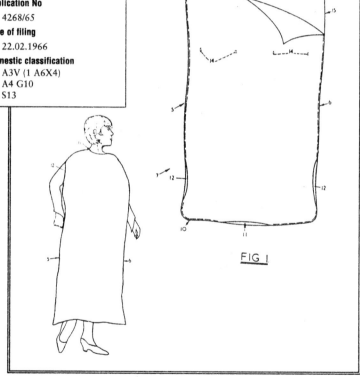

FIG 1

Improvements in Garments

According to this invention there is provided a garment of bag form and apertured at selected locations to serve the dual purpose of being a dressing gown and forming the top and bottom sheets for a bed. It is considered that in the application of the garment when it serves as the top and bottom sheets for a bed, it will have particular use for people visiting for only one night or a short spell, in that it will protect the blankets of a bed and so reduce the amount of laundering required to accommodate such visitors.

Additionally it is considered that the extended portion of the bag beyond the open end thereof may be folded back upon itself and stitched or otherwise provided with means for closure of the sides thereof so that it forms a pocket for the accommodation of a pillow.

An Improved Protective Coat for Sheep

Many sheep and their lambs are lost by reason of the inclement weather to which they are often subjected and the present invention has for its object to provide a simple and cheap protective coat whereby the loss of sheep from this source will be minimised.

According to this invention a protective coat comprises a body portion adapted to cover the back and sides of a sheep, the body portion being closed at its forward end but for an opening through which the sheep's head can be introduced, and a rear portion sewn or otherwise secured to the rear of the body portion, the said coat being adapted to be secured to the sheep by sewing it to the wool, thus rendering unnecessary straps and buckles or like securing means and giving the sheep complete freedom of movement.

The improved coat may be made of jute, canvas or of suitable cloth. It is believed that jute is the most satisfactory material, both because it is the most economic and because it breathes easily.

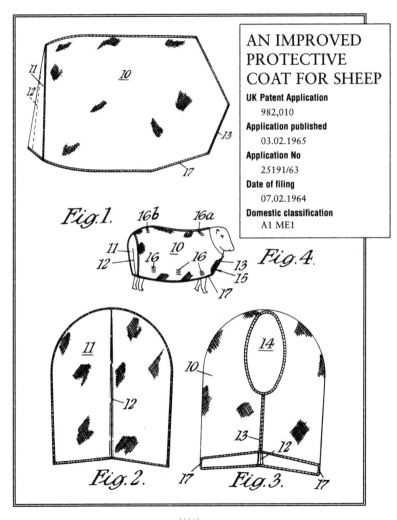

AN IMPROVED PROTECTIVE COAT FOR SHEEP

UK Patent Application
982,010

Application published
03.02.1965

Application No
25191/63

Date of filing
07.02.1964

Domestic classification
A1 ME1

Fig.1.

Fig.4.

Fig.2.

Fig.3.

IMPROVEMENTS IN SLEEVED GARMENTS

UK Patent Application
  GB 891 760

Application published
  21.03.1962

Application No
  21565/57

Date of filing
  08.07.1958

Domestic classification
  CLASS 43, LX

FIG. 1.

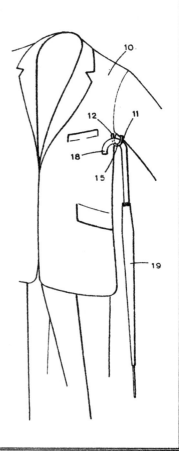

FIG. 2.

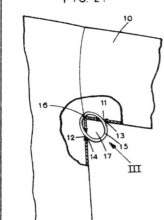

Improvements in Sleeved Garments

This invention relates to improved sleeved garments, and especially, but not exclusively, to men's jackets or overcoats.

It is frequently necessary to carry an umbrella for reasons either of fashion or protection against the weather and the disposal of this often becomes vexatious when both hands are required for other purposes and when to even hang the crook of the umbrella over one arm is not wholly convenient. It is an object of the invention to provide means whereby the umbrella, or any other article, may be conveniently carried in order to free the hands. It will be appreciated that not only a walking-stick, but any article provided with a hook or other suitable means can be similarly carried.

The invention may also be applied to women's garments such as jackets, and may be arranged to support a handbag, which in any case is frequently carried under the wearer's arm. The wearer's hands are thus left free and the handbag or other article is safeguarded against being dropped or accidentally displaced or lost.

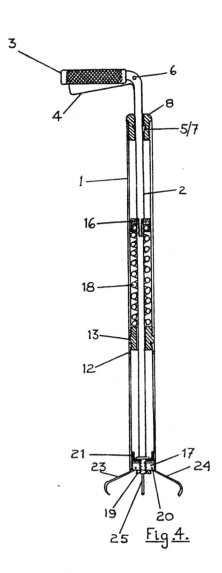

Fig.4.